The World of
CHARLES RENNIE MACKINTOSH

Pomegranate
SAN FRANCISCO

POMEGRANATE COMMUNICATIONS, INC.
BOX 6099, ROHNERT PARK, CA 94927
800-227-1428; WWW.POMEGRANATE.COM

POMEGRANATE EUROPE LTD.
FULLBRIDGE HOUSE, FULLBRIDGE
MALDON, ESSEX CM9 4LE, ENGLAND

POMEGRANATE CATALOG NO. A947
ISBN 0-7649-1380-8

DESIGNED BY SHANNON LEMME

PRINTED IN CHINA
FIRST EDITION
09 08 07 06 05 04 03   10 9 8 7 6 5 4 3 2

n the early 1900s young architects and designers in Europe and North America were searching for a new vocabulary to express their ideas and aims for the new century. None achieved this more radically than the young Scot from Glasgow, Charles Rennie Mackintosh (1868–1928). Mackintosh had trained as an architect but was also an accomplished artist, particularly in watercolor. He believed that the values and qualities of "art" should be foremost, that the architect and designer should think as an artist before putting pencil to paper.

Mackintosh also believed wholeheartedly in the unity and entity of his work. As an architect he wished to be responsible for all the elements of a project—furniture, carpets, wall decorations, light fittings, even cutlery and tableware. This control gave his interiors an intensely personal and coherent appearance, creating works of art that continually crossed the thresholds between painting, architecture, and design. Nowhere was this more powerful than in the rooms he created for exhibitions in Vienna, Berlin, Cologne, and Turin, and in the exquisite tea rooms he designed in Glasgow for the astute Kate Cranston.

Mackintosh painted in watercolor throughout his life, most productively in the early years of his career and the later ones, when his architectural output was small. The paintings of the 1890s have a mysterious and subtle imagery, reflecting Mackintosh's personal circumstances as well as the symbolist literature that fascinated him. After Mackintosh left Glasgow, settling in London in 1915, his architectural practice collapsed and he began to produce more finished watercolors in the hopes of making a living. Drawing on his earlier botanical sketches, he produced paintings of cut flowers and a series of designs for textiles, with which he had considerable success.

Mackintosh often collaborated on projects with his wife, Margaret Macdonald, and her sister, Francis Macdonald; both women were skilled painters and decorative artists in their own right. Margaret Macdonald's art-works deeply impressed Mackintosh, inspiring his interest in painting and the decorative arts. Along with their shared works, the Macdonalds individually exhibited their watercolors and designs. The two sisters had studied at Glasgow School of Art between 1890 and 1894.

In 1923, after failing to reestablish himself as an architect in London, Mackintosh and his wife settled in France, traveling between the villages of France and Spain that span the Pyrenean border. Some of Mackintosh's most satisfying and beautiful paintings were made in this peaceful countryside, away from the artistic infighting of London in the 1920s.

Sadly, in 1928, Mackintosh died before achieving his ambition of a London exhibition of watercolors. These paintings now form one of the most popular elements of his legacy, reinforcing his unique artistic approach to architecture and design.

—Roger Billcliffe

• • • • PEONIES, c. 1919–1920 • • • •

PENCIL AND WATERCOLOR, 42.8 x 42.6 CM (16⅞ x 16¾ IN.)
COLLECTION: METROPOLITAN MUSEUM OF ART, NEW YORK

••••• TULIP AND LATTICE—DIAGONAL, c. 1916–1919 •••••

PENCIL AND WATERCOLOR, 24.5 x 20.4 CM (9⅝ x 8 IN.)
COLLECTION: BRITISH MUSEUM

NAME	PHONE (H)
ADDRESS	PHONE (W)
	FAX
EMAIL	CELL/PAGER

NAME	PHONE (H)
ADDRESS	PHONE (W)
	FAX
EMAIL	CELL/PAGER

NAME	PHONE (H)
ADDRESS	PHONE (W)
	FAX
EMAIL	CELL/PAGER

NAME	PHONE (H)
ADDRESS	PHONE (W)
	FAX
EMAIL	CELL/PAGER

NAME	PHONE (H)
ADDRESS	PHONE (W)
	FAX
EMAIL	CELL/PAGER

NAME

ADDRESS

EMAIL

PHONE (H)

PHONE (W)

FAX

CELL/PAGER

NAME

ADDRESS

EMAIL

PHONE (H)

PHONE (W)

FAX

CELL/PAGER

NAME

ADDRESS

EMAIL

PHONE (H)

PHONE (W)

FAX

CELL/PAGER

NAME

ADDRESS

EMAIL

PHONE (H)

PHONE (W)

FAX

CELL/PAGER

NAME

ADDRESS

EMAIL

PHONE (H)

PHONE (W)

FAX

CELL/PAGER

NAME   PHONE (H)

ADDRESS   PHONE (W)

                                              FAX

EMAIL   CELL/PAGER

NAME   PHONE (H)

ADDRESS   PHONE (W)

                                              FAX

EMAIL   CELL/PAGER

NAME   PHONE (H)

ADDRESS   PHONE (W)

                                              FAX

EMAIL   CELL/PAGER

NAME   PHONE (H)

ADDRESS   PHONE (W)

                                              FAX

EMAIL   CELL/PAGER

NAME   PHONE (H)

ADDRESS   PHONE (W)

                                              FAX

EMAIL   CELL/PAGER

NAME   PHONE (H)

ADDRESS   PHONE (W)

                                              FAX

EMAIL   CELL/PAGER

NAME

ADDRESS

EMAIL

PHONE (H)

PHONE (W)

FAX

CELL/PAGER

NAME

ADDRESS

EMAIL

PHONE (H)

PHONE (W)

FAX

CELL/PAGER

NAME

ADDRESS

EMAIL

PHONE (H)

PHONE (W)

FAX

CELL/PAGER

NAME

ADDRESS

EMAIL

PHONE (H)

PHONE (W)

FAX

CELL/PAGER

NAME

ADDRESS

EMAIL

PHONE (H)

PHONE (W)

FAX

CELL/PAGER

NAME

ADDRESS

EMAIL

PHONE (H)

PHONE (W)

FAX

CELL/PAGER

• • • • A Hill Town in Southern France, c. 1924–1926 • • • •
WATERCOLOR, 42 x 42 cm (16½ x 16½ in.)
PRIVATE COLLECTION

• • • • HOUSE FOR AN ART LOVER: DESIGN FOR THE DINING ROOM • • • •

LITHOGRAPH OF MACKINTOSH'S ORIGINAL COMPETITION DRAWING, PART OF THE PORTFOLIO
PUBLISHED BY ALEXANDER KOCH IN 1902

NAME

PHONE (H)

ADDRESS

PHONE (W)

FAX

EMAIL

CELL/PAGER

NAME

PHONE (H)

ADDRESS

PHONE (W)

FAX

EMAIL

CELL/PAGER

NAME

PHONE (H)

ADDRESS

PHONE (W)

FAX

EMAIL

CELL/PAGER

NAME

PHONE (H)

ADDRESS

PHONE (W)

FAX

EMAIL

CELL/PAGER

NAME

PHONE (H)

ADDRESS

PHONE (W)

FAX

EMAIL

CELL/PAGER

NAME

ADDRESS

EMAIL

PHONE (H)

PHONE (W)

FAX

CELL/PAGER

NAME

ADDRESS

EMAIL

PHONE (H)

PHONE (W)

FAX

CELL/PAGER

NAME

ADDRESS

EMAIL

PHONE (H)

PHONE (W)

FAX

CELL/PAGER

NAME

ADDRESS

EMAIL

PHONE (H)

PHONE (W)

FAX

CELL/PAGER

NAME

ADDRESS

EMAIL

PHONE (H)

PHONE (W)

FAX

CELL/PAGER

NAME   PHONE (H)

ADDRESS   PHONE (W)

                                               FAX

EMAIL   CELL/PAGER

NAME   PHONE (H)

ADDRESS   PHONE (W)

                                               FAX

EMAIL   CELL/PAGER

NAME   PHONE (H)

ADDRESS   PHONE (W)

                                               FAX

EMAIL   CELL/PAGER

NAME   PHONE (H)

ADDRESS   PHONE (W)

                                               FAX

EMAIL   CELL/PAGER

NAME   PHONE (H)

ADDRESS   PHONE (W)

                                               FAX

EMAIL   CELL/PAGER

NAME   PHONE (H)

ADDRESS   PHONE (W)

                                               FAX

EMAIL   CELL/PAGER

NAME

ADDRESS

EMAIL

PHONE (H)

PHONE (W)

FAX

CELL/PAGER

NAME

ADDRESS

EMAIL

PHONE (H)

PHONE (W)

FAX

CELL/PAGER

NAME

ADDRESS

EMAIL

PHONE (H)

PHONE (W)

FAX

CELL/PAGER

NAME

ADDRESS

EMAIL

PHONE (H)

PHONE (W)

FAX

CELL/PAGER

NAME

ADDRESS

EMAIL

PHONE (H)

PHONE (W)

FAX

CELL/PAGER

NAME

ADDRESS

EMAIL

PHONE (H)

PHONE (W)

FAX

CELL/PAGER

• • • • WHITE TULIPS, c. 1918–1920 • • • •
PENCIL AND WATERCOLOR, 40.5 x 35.2 cm (15¹⁵⁄₁₆ x 13⅞ in.)
PRIVATE COLLECTION

.... STENCIL DECORATION FOR MACKINTOSH'S ROOM EXHIBIT
AT THE EIGHTH EXHIBITION FOR THE VIENNA SECESSION, 1900 ....

ILLUSTRATED IN THE MAGAZINE OF THE SECESSION, *VER SACRUM*, NUMBER 23, 1901
LITHOGRAPH, 14.9 x 14.9 CM (5 7/8 x 5 7/8 IN.)

NAME

ADDRESS

EMAIL

PHONE (H)

PHONE (W)

FAX

CELL/PAGER

NAME

ADDRESS

EMAIL

PHONE (H)

PHONE (W)

FAX

CELL/PAGER

NAME

ADDRESS

EMAIL

PHONE (H)

PHONE (W)

FAX

CELL/PAGER

NAME

ADDRESS

EMAIL

PHONE (H)

PHONE (W)

FAX

CELL/PAGER

NAME

ADDRESS

EMAIL

PHONE (H)

PHONE (W)

FAX

CELL/PAGER

NAME

ADDRESS

EMAIL

PHONE (H)

PHONE (W)

FAX

CELL/PAGER

NAME   PHONE (H)

ADDRESS   PHONE (W)

                                                  FAX

EMAIL   CELL/PAGER

NAME   PHONE (H)

ADDRESS   PHONE (W)

                                                  FAX

EMAIL   CELL/PAGER

NAME   PHONE (H)

ADDRESS   PHONE (W)

                                                  FAX

EMAIL   CELL/PAGER

NAME   PHONE (H)

ADDRESS   PHONE (W)

                                                  FAX

EMAIL   CELL/PAGER

NAME   PHONE (H)

ADDRESS   PHONE (W)

                                                  FAX

EMAIL   CELL/PAGER

NAME   PHONE (H)

ADDRESS   PHONE (W)

                                                  FAX

EMAIL   CELL/PAGER

NAME   PHONE (H)

ADDRESS   PHONE (W)

FAX

EMAIL   CELL/PAGER

NAME   PHONE (H)

ADDRESS   PHONE (W)

FAX

EMAIL   CELL/PAGER

NAME   PHONE (H)

ADDRESS   PHONE (W)

FAX

EMAIL   CELL/PAGER

NAME   PHONE (H)

ADDRESS   PHONE (W)

FAX

EMAIL   CELL/PAGER

NAME   PHONE (H)

ADDRESS   PHONE (W)

FAX

EMAIL   CELL/PAGER

NAME   PHONE (H)

ADDRESS   PHONE (W)

FAX

EMAIL   CELL/PAGER

NAME

ADDRESS

EMAIL

PHONE (H)

PHONE (W)

FAX

CELL/PAGER

NAME

ADDRESS

EMAIL

PHONE (H)

PHONE (W)

FAX

CELL/PAGER

NAME

ADDRESS

EMAIL

PHONE (H)

PHONE (W)

FAX

CELL/PAGER

NAME

ADDRESS

EMAIL

PHONE (H)

PHONE (W)

FAX

CELL/PAGER

NAME

ADDRESS

EMAIL

PHONE (H)

PHONE (W)

FAX

CELL/PAGER

NAME

ADDRESS

EMAIL

PHONE (H)

PHONE (W)

FAX

CELL/PAGER

• • • • BORAGE, WALBERSWICK, 1914 • • • •

PENCIL AND WATERCOLOR, 25.8 x 20.2 CM (10 3/16 x 8 IN.)

PRIVATE COLLECTION

• • • • SUMMER IN THE SOUTH, C. 1924–1927 • • • •

WATERCOLOR, 28.3 x 38.5 CM (11⅛ x 15⅛ IN.)

PRIVATE COLLECTION

NAME _____ PHONE (H) _____

ADDRESS _____ PHONE (W) _____

_____ FAX _____

EMAIL _____ CELL/PAGER _____

NAME _____ PHONE (H) _____

ADDRESS _____ PHONE (W) _____

_____ FAX _____

EMAIL _____ CELL/PAGER _____

NAME _____ PHONE (H) _____

ADDRESS _____ PHONE (W) _____

_____ FAX _____

EMAIL _____ CELL/PAGER _____

NAME _____ PHONE (H) _____

ADDRESS _____ PHONE (W) _____

_____ FAX _____

EMAIL _____ CELL/PAGER _____

NAME _____ PHONE (H) _____

ADDRESS _____ PHONE (W) _____

_____ FAX _____

EMAIL _____ CELL/PAGER _____

NAME _____ PHONE (H) _____

ADDRESS _____ PHONE (W) _____

_____ FAX _____

EMAIL _____ CELL/PAGER _____

NAME

ADDRESS

EMAIL

PHONE (H)

PHONE (W)

FAX

CELL/PAGER

NAME

ADDRESS

EMAIL

PHONE (H)

PHONE (W)

FAX

CELL/PAGER

NAME

ADDRESS

EMAIL

PHONE (H)

PHONE (W)

FAX

CELL/PAGER

NAME

ADDRESS

EMAIL

PHONE (H)

PHONE (W)

FAX

CELL/PAGER

NAME

ADDRESS

EMAIL

PHONE (H)

PHONE (W)

FAX

CELL/PAGER

NAME

ADDRESS

EMAIL

PHONE (H)

PHONE (W)

FAX

CELL/PAGER

NAME

ADDRESS

EMAIL

PHONE (H)

PHONE (W)

FAX

CELL/PAGER

NAME

ADDRESS

EMAIL

PHONE (H)

PHONE (W)

FAX

CELL/PAGER

NAME

ADDRESS

EMAIL

PHONE (H)

PHONE (W)

FAX

CELL/PAGER

NAME

ADDRESS

EMAIL

PHONE (H)

PHONE (W)

FAX

CELL/PAGER

NAME

ADDRESS

EMAIL

PHONE (H)

PHONE (W)

FAX

CELL/PAGER

NAME

ADDRESS

EMAIL

PHONE (H)

PHONE (W)

FAX

CELL/PAGER

NAME   PHONE (H)

ADDRESS   PHONE (W)

                                            FAX

EMAIL   CELL/PAGER

NAME   PHONE (H)

ADDRESS   PHONE (W)

                                            FAX

EMAIL   CELL/PAGER

NAME   PHONE (H)

ADDRESS   PHONE (W)

                                            FAX

EMAIL   CELL/PAGER

NAME   PHONE (H)

ADDRESS   PHONE (W)

                                            FAX

EMAIL   CELL/PAGER

NAME   PHONE (H)

ADDRESS   PHONE (W)

                                            FAX

EMAIL   CELL/PAGER

NAME   PHONE (H)

ADDRESS   PHONE (W)

                                            FAX

EMAIL   CELL/PAGER

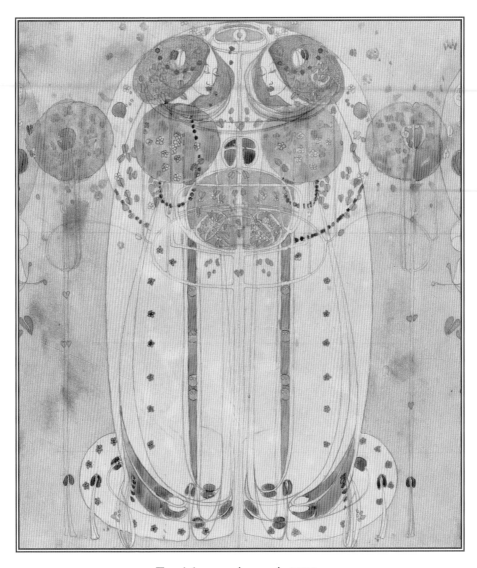

• • • • THE WASSAIL (DETAIL), 1900 • • • •

PENCIL AND WATERCOLOR ON TRACING PAPER, 32 x 68 cm (12⅝ x 26¾ in.)
PRIVATE COLLECTION

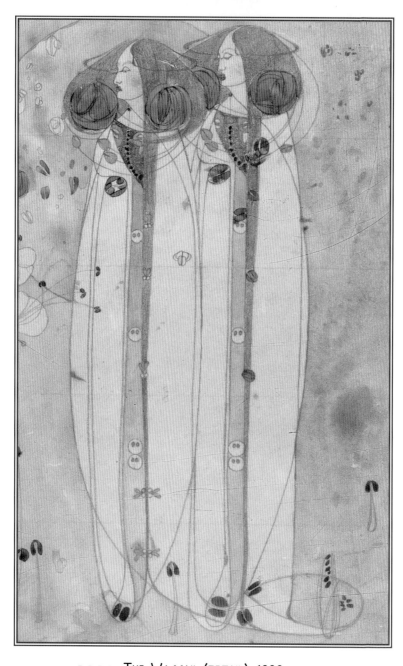

• • • • THE WASSAIL (DETAIL), 1900 • • • •

PENCIL AND WATERCOLOR ON TRACING PAPER, 32 x 68 CM (12⅝ x 26¾ IN.)
PRIVATE COLLECTION

NAME   PHONE (H)

ADDRESS   PHONE (W)

                                        FAX

EMAIL   CELL/PAGER

NAME   PHONE (H)

ADDRESS   PHONE (W)

                                        FAX

EMAIL   CELL/PAGER

NAME   PHONE (H)

ADDRESS   PHONE (W)

                                        FAX

EMAIL   CELL/PAGER

NAME   PHONE (H)

ADDRESS   PHONE (W)

                                        FAX

EMAIL   CELL/PAGER

NAME   PHONE (H)

ADDRESS   PHONE (W)

                                        FAX

EMAIL   CELL/PAGER

NAME   PHONE (H)

ADDRESS   PHONE (W)

                                        FAX

EMAIL   CELL/PAGER

NAME	PHONE (H)
ADDRESS	PHONE (W)
	FAX
EMAIL	CELL/PAGER

NAME	PHONE (H)
ADDRESS	PHONE (W)
	FAX
EMAIL	CELL/PAGER

NAME	PHONE (H)
ADDRESS	PHONE (W)
	FAX
EMAIL	CELL/PAGER

NAME	PHONE (H)
ADDRESS	PHONE (W)
	FAX
EMAIL	CELL/PAGER

NAME	PHONE (H)
ADDRESS	PHONE (W)
	FAX
EMAIL	CELL/PAGER

NAME	PHONE (H)
ADDRESS	PHONE (W)
	FAX
EMAIL	CELL/PAGER

NAME

ADDRESS

EMAIL

PHONE (H)

PHONE (W)

FAX

CELL/PAGER

NAME

ADDRESS

EMAIL

PHONE (H)

PHONE (W)

FAX

CELL/PAGER

NAME

ADDRESS

EMAIL

PHONE (H)

PHONE (W)

FAX

CELL/PAGER

NAME

ADDRESS

EMAIL

PHONE (H)

PHONE (W)

FAX

CELL/PAGER

NAME

ADDRESS

EMAIL

PHONE (H)

PHONE (W)

FAX

CELL/PAGER

NAME

ADDRESS

EMAIL

PHONE (H)

PHONE (W)

FAX

CELL/PAGER

NAME

ADDRESS

EMAIL

PHONE (H)

PHONE (W)

FAX

CELL/PAGER

NAME

ADDRESS

EMAIL

PHONE (H)

PHONE (W)

FAX

CELL/PAGER

NAME

ADDRESS

EMAIL

PHONE (H)

PHONE (W)

FAX

CELL/PAGER

NAME

ADDRESS

EMAIL

PHONE (H)

PHONE (W)

FAX

CELL/PAGER

NAME

ADDRESS

EMAIL

PHONE (H)

PHONE (W)

FAX

CELL/PAGER

NAME

ADDRESS

EMAIL

PHONE (H)

PHONE (W)

FAX

CELL/PAGER

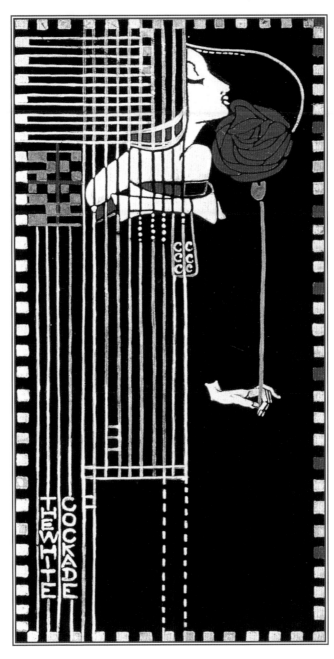

MENU CARD FOR KATE CRANSTON'S WHITE COCKADE TEA ROOMS (DETAIL), 1911
MARGARET MACDONALD MACKINTOSH
21.8 x 31.6 CM (8⅝ x 12½ IN.)
PRIVATE COLLECTION

• • • • BLACKTHORN, CHIDDINGSTONE, 1910 • • • •

PENCIL AND WATERCOLOR, 25.8 x 20 CM (10⅛ x 7 ⅞ IN.)
PRIVATE COLLECTION

NAME	PHONE (H)
ADDRESS .	PHONE (W)
	FAX
EMAIL	CELL/PAGER

NAME	PHONE (H)
ADDRESS	PHONE (W)
	FAX
EMAIL	CELL/PAGER

NAME	PHONE (H)
ADDRESS	PHONE (W)
	FAX
EMAIL	CELL/PAGER

NAME	PHONE (H)
ADDRESS	PHONE (W)
	FAX
EMAIL	CELL/PAGER

NAME	PHONE (H)
ADDRESS	PHONE (W)
	FAX
EMAIL,	CELL/PAGER

NAME

ADDRESS

EMAIL

PHONE (H)

PHONE (W)

FAX

CELL/PAGER

NAME

ADDRESS

EMAIL

PHONE (H)

PHONE (W)

FAX

CELL/PAGER

NAME

ADDRESS

EMAIL

PHONE (H)

PHONE (W)

FAX

CELL/PAGER

NAME

ADDRESS

EMAIL

PHONE (H)

PHONE (W)

FAX

CELL/PAGER

NAME

ADDRESS

EMAIL

PHONE (H)

PHONE (W)

FAX

CELL/PAGER

NAME

ADDRESS

EMAIL

PHONE (H)

PHONE (W)

FAX

CELL/PAGER

NAME

ADDRESS

EMAIL

PHONE (H)

PHONE (W)

FAX

CELL/PAGER

NAME

ADDRESS

EMAIL

PHONE (H)

PHONE (W)

FAX

CELL/PAGER

NAME

ADDRESS

EMAIL

PHONE (H)

PHONE (W)

FAX

CELL/PAGER

NAME

ADDRESS

EMAIL

PHONE (H)

PHONE (W)

FAX

CELL/PAGER

NAME

ADDRESS

EMAIL

PHONE (H)

PHONE (W)

FAX

CELL/PAGER

NAME

ADDRESS

EMAIL

PHONE (H)

PHONE (W)

FAX

CELL/PAGER

NAME

ADDRESS

EMAIL

PHONE (H)

PHONE (W)

FAX

CELL/PAGER

NAME

ADDRESS

EMAIL

PHONE (H)

PHONE (W)

FAX

CELL/PAGER

NAME

ADDRESS

EMAIL

PHONE (H)

PHONE (W)

FAX

CELL/PAGER

NAME

ADDRESS

EMAIL

PHONE (H)

PHONE (W)

FAX

CELL/PAGER

NAME

ADDRESS

EMAIL

PHONE (H)

PHONE (W)

FAX

CELL/PAGER

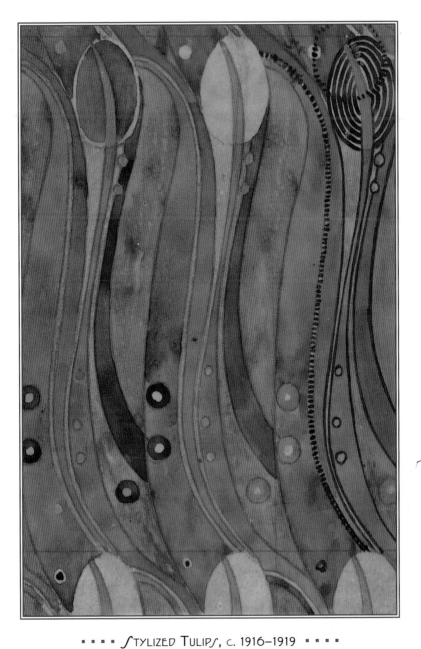

••••• STYLIZED TULIPS, c. 1916–1919 •••••

PENCIL AND WATERCOLOR ON TRACING PAPER, 29.8 x 21.7 CM (11¾ x 8½ IN.)
PRIVATE COLLECTION

. . . . . BLUE AND PINK TOBACCO FLOWERS, C. 1916–1919 . . . .

PENCIL, WATERCOLOR, AND GOUACHE, 56 x 36.5 CM (22¹⁄₁₆ x 14⅜ IN.)
PRIVATE COLLECTION

NAME	PHONE (H)
ADDRESS	PHONE (W)
	FAX
EMAIL	CELL/PAGER

NAME	PHONE (H)
ADDRESS	PHONE (W)
	FAX
EMAIL	CELL/PAGER

NAME	PHONE (H)
ADDRESS	PHONE (W)
	FAX
EMAIL	CELL/PAGER

NAME	PHONE (H)
ADDRESS	PHONE (W)
	FAX
EMAIL	CELL/PAGER

NAME _____ PHONE (H) _____

ADDRESS _____ PHONE (W) _____

_____ FAX _____

EMAIL _____ CELL/PAGER _____

NAME _____ PHONE (H) _____

ADDRESS _____ PHONE (W) _____

_____ FAX _____

EMAIL _____ CELL/PAGER _____

NAME _____ PHONE (H) _____

ADDRESS _____ PHONE (W) _____

_____ FAX _____

EMAIL _____ CELL/PAGER _____

NAME _____ PHONE (H) _____

ADDRESS _____ PHONE (W) _____

_____ FAX _____

EMAIL _____ CELL/PAGER _____

NAME

ADDRESS

EMAIL

PHONE (H)

PHONE (W)

FAX

CELL/PAGER

NAME

ADDRESS

EMAIL

PHONE (H)

PHONE (W)

FAX

CELL/PAGER

NAME

ADDRESS

EMAIL

PHONE (H)

PHONE (W)

FAX

CELL/PAGER

NAME

ADDRESS

EMAIL

PHONE (H)

PHONE (W)

FAX

CELL/PAGER

NAME

ADDRESS

EMAIL

PHONE (H)

PHONE (W)

FAX

CELL/PAGER

NAME

ADDRESS

EMAIL

PHONE (H)

PHONE (W)

FAX

CELL/PAGER

NAME

ADDRESS

EMAIL

PHONE (H)

PHONE (W)

FAX

CELL/PAGER

NAME

ADDRESS

EMAIL

PHONE (H)

PHONE (W)

FAX

CELL/PAGER

NAME

ADDRESS

EMAIL

PHONE (H)

PHONE (W)

FAX

CELL/PAGER

NAME

ADDRESS

EMAIL

PHONE (H)

PHONE (W)

FAX

CELL/PAGER

NAME

ADDRESS

EMAIL

PHONE (H)

PHONE (W)

FAX

CELL/PAGER

NAME

ADDRESS

EMAIL

PHONE (H)

PHONE (W)

FAX

CELL/PAGER

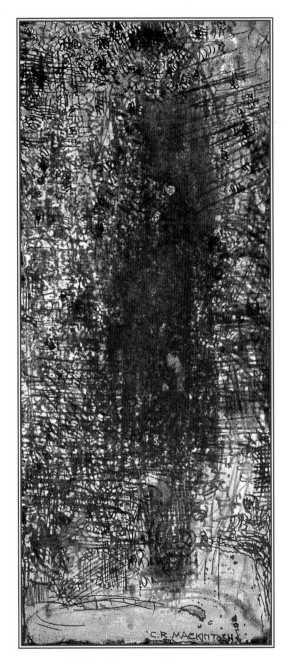

• • • • A ſOUTHERN TOWN, c. 1924–1927 • • • •

WATERCOLOR, 32.2 x 37.6 cm (12⅝ x 14¹³⁄₁₆ in.)
COLLECTION: HUNTERIAN ART GALLERY, UNIVERSITY OF GLASGOW

NAME

ADDRESS

EMAIL

PHONE (H)

PHONE (W)

FAX

CELL/PAGER

NAME

ADDRESS

EMAIL

PHONE (H)

PHONE (W)

FAX

CELL/PAGER

NAME

ADDRESS

EMAIL

PHONE (H)

PHONE (W)

FAX

CELL/PAGER

NAME

ADDRESS

EMAIL

PHONE (H)

PHONE (W)

FAX

CELL/PAGER

NAME

ADDRESS

EMAIL

PHONE (H)

PHONE (W)

FAX

CELL/PAGER

NAME

ADDRESS

EMAIL

PHONE (H)

PHONE (W)

FAX

CELL/PAGER

NAME

ADDRESS

EMAIL

PHONE (H)

PHONE (W)

FAX

CELL/PAGER

NAME

ADDRESS

EMAIL

PHONE (H)

PHONE (W)

FAX

CELL/PAGER

NAME

ADDRESS

EMAIL

PHONE (H)

PHONE (W)

FAX

CELL/PAGER

NAME

ADDRESS

EMAIL

PHONE (H)

PHONE (W)

FAX

CELL/PAGER

NAME

ADDRESS

EMAIL

PHONE (H)

PHONE (W)

FAX

CELL/PAGER

NAME

ADDRESS

EMAIL

PHONE (H)

PHONE (W)

FAX

CELL/PAGER

NAME _____ PHONE (H) _____

ADDRESS _____ PHONE (W) _____

_____ FAX _____

EMAIL _____ CELL/PAGER _____

NAME _____ PHONE (H) _____

ADDRESS _____ PHONE (W) _____

_____ FAX _____

EMAIL _____ CELL/PAGER _____

NAME _____ PHONE (H) _____

ADDRESS _____ PHONE (W) _____

_____ FAX _____

EMAIL _____ CELL/PAGER _____

NAME _____ PHONE (H) _____

ADDRESS _____ PHONE (W) _____

_____ FAX _____

EMAIL _____ CELL/PAGER _____

NAME _____ PHONE (H) _____

ADDRESS _____ PHONE (W) _____

_____ FAX _____

EMAIL _____ CELL/PAGER _____

NAME _____ PHONE (H) _____

ADDRESS _____ PHONE (W) _____

_____ FAX _____

EMAIL _____ CELL/PAGER _____

NAME

ADDRESS

EMAIL

PHONE (H)

PHONE (W)

FAX

CELL/PAGER

NAME

ADDRESS

EMAIL

PHONE (H)

PHONE (W)

FAX

CELL/PAGER

NAME

ADDRESS

EMAIL

PHONE (H)

PHONE (W)

FAX

CELL/PAGER

NAME

ADDRESS

EMAIL

PHONE (H)

PHONE (W)

FAX

CELL/PAGER

NAME

ADDRESS

EMAIL

PHONE (H)

PHONE (W)

FAX

CELL/PAGER

NAME

ADDRESS

EMAIL

PHONE (H)

PHONE (W)

FAX

CELL/PAGER

•••• CYCLAMEN, c. 1922–1923 ••••
WATERCOLOR, 37 x 42 CM (14½ x 16½ IN.)
PRIVATE COLLECTION

COLLIOURE, PYRÉNÉES-ORIENTALES:
SUMMER PALACE OF THE QUEENS OF ARAGON, c. 1924–1926

WATERCOLOR, 38 x 43 CM (14¹⁵⁄₁₆ x 16¹⁵⁄₁₆ IN.)
COLLECTION: NATIONAL TRUST FOR SCOTLAND

NAME	PHONE (H)
ADDRESS	PHONE (W)
	FAX
EMAIL	CELL/PAGER

NAME	PHONE (H)
ADDRESS	PHONE (W)
	FAX
EMAIL	CELL/PAGER

NAME	PHONE (H)
ADDRESS	PHONE (W)
	FAX
EMAIL	CELL/PAGER

NAME	PHONE (H)
ADDRESS	PHONE (W)
	FAX
EMAIL	CELL/PAGER

NAME

ADDRESS

EMAIL

PHONE (H)

PHONE (W)

FAX

CELL/PAGER

NAME

ADDRESS

EMAIL

PHONE (H)

PHONE (W)

FAX

CELL/PAGER

NAME

ADDRESS

EMAIL

PHONE (H)

PHONE (W)

FAX

CELL/PAGER

NAME

ADDRESS

EMAIL

PHONE (H)

PHONE (W)

FAX

CELL/PAGER

NAME

ADDRESS

EMAIL

PHONE (H)

PHONE (W)

FAX

CELL/PAGER

NAME

ADDRESS

EMAIL

PHONE (H)

PHONE (W)

FAX

CELL/PAGER

NAME

ADDRESS

EMAIL

PHONE (H)

PHONE (W)

FAX

CELL/PAGER

NAME

ADDRESS

EMAIL

PHONE (H)

PHONE (W)

FAX

CELL/PAGER

NAME

ADDRESS

EMAIL

PHONE (H)

PHONE (W)

FAX

CELL/PAGER

NAME

ADDRESS

EMAIL

PHONE (H)

PHONE (W)

FAX

CELL/PAGER

NAME

ADDRESS

EMAIL

PHONE (H)

PHONE (W)

FAX

CELL/PAGER

NAME

ADDRESS

EMAIL

PHONE (H)

PHONE (W)

FAX

CELL/PAGER

NAME

ADDRESS

EMAIL

PHONE (H)

PHONE (W)

FAX

CELL/PAGER

NAME

ADDRESS

EMAIL

PHONE (H)

PHONE (W)

FAX

CELL/PAGER

NAME

ADDRESS

EMAIL

PHONE (H)

PHONE (W)

FAX

CELL/PAGER

NAME

ADDRESS

EMAIL

PHONE (H)

PHONE (W)

FAX

CELL/PAGER

• • • • YᴇʟʟOW TᴜʟIᴘꜱ, ᴄ. 1922–1923 • • • •

WATERCOLOR, 49.5 x 49.5 ᴄᴍ (19½ x 19½ ɪɴ.)
PRIVATE COLLECTION

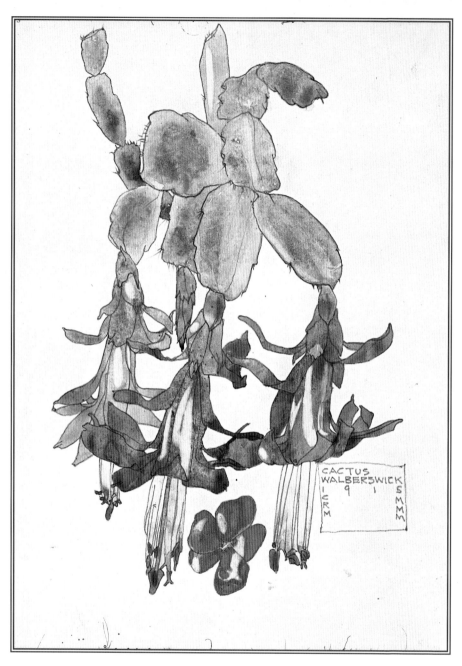

•••• Cactus Flower, Walberswick, 1915 ••••

PENCIL AND WATERCOLOR, 25.8 × 20.2 cm (10³/₁₆ × 7¹⁵/₁₆ IN.)

COLLECTION: SHEFFIELD CITY ART GALLERIES AND MUSEUMS

NAME	PHONE (H)
ADDRESS	PHONE (W)
	FAX
EMAIL	CELL/PAGER

NAME	PHONE (H)
ADDRESS	PHONE (W)
	FAX
EMAIL	CELL/PAGER

NAME	PHONE (H)
ADDRESS	PHONE (W)
	FAX
EMAIL	CELL/PAGER

NAME	PHONE (H)
ADDRESS	PHONE (W)
	FAX
EMAIL	CELL/PAGER

NAME	PHONE (H)
ADDRESS	PHONE (W)
	FAX
EMAIL	CELL/PAGER

NAME

ADDRESS

EMAIL

PHONE (H)

PHONE (W)

FAX

CELL/PAGER

NAME

ADDRESS

EMAIL

PHONE (H)

PHONE (W)

FAX

CELL/PAGER

NAME

ADDRESS

EMAIL

PHONE (H)

PHONE (W)

FAX

CELL/PAGER

NAME

ADDRESS

EMAIL

PHONE (H)

PHONE (W)

FAX

CELL/PAGER

NAME

ADDRESS

EMAIL

PHONE (H)

PHONE (W)

FAX

CELL/PAGER

NAME   PHONE (H)

ADDRESS   PHONE (W)

FAX

EMAIL   CELL/PAGER

NAME   PHONE (H)

ADDRESS   PHONE (W)

FAX

EMAIL   CELL/PAGER

NAME   PHONE (H)

ADDRESS   PHONE (W)

FAX

EMAIL   CELL/PAGER

NAME   PHONE (H)

ADDRESS   PHONE (W)

FAX

EMAIL   CELL/PAGER

NAME   PHONE (H)

ADDRESS   PHONE (W)

FAX

EMAIL   CELL/PAGER

NAME   PHONE (H)

ADDRESS   PHONE (W)

FAX

EMAIL   CELL/PAGER

NAME

ADDRESS

EMAIL

PHONE (H)

PHONE (W)

FAX

CELL/PAGER

NAME

ADDRESS

EMAIL

PHONE (H)

PHONE (W)

FAX

CELL/PAGER

NAME

ADDRESS

EMAIL

PHONE (H)

PHONE (W)

FAX

CELL/PAGER

NAME

ADDRESS

EMAIL

PHONE (H)

PHONE (W)

FAX

CELL/PAGER

NAME

ADDRESS

EMAIL

PHONE (H)

PHONE (W)

FAX

CELL/PAGER

NAME

ADDRESS

EMAIL

PHONE (H)

PHONE (W)

FAX

CELL/PAGER

• • • • STYLIZED ROSES—CHIFFON VOILÉ • • • •
MARGARET MACDONALD MACKINTOSH
PENCIL AND WATERCOLOR ON TRACING PAPER, 25 x 20 CM (9¹³⁄₁₆ x 7⅞ IN.)
PRIVATE COLLECTION

····· MIXED FLOWERS, MONT LOUIS, 1925 ·····

PENCIL AND WATERCOLOR, 26.2 x 20.5 CM (10⁵⁄₁₆ x 8¹⁄₁₆ IN.)

COLLECTION: BRITISH MUSEUM

NAME

ADDRESS

EMAIL

PHONE (H)

PHONE (W)

FAX

CELL/PAGER

NAME

ADDRESS

EMAIL

PHONE (H)

PHONE (W)

FAX

CELL/PAGER

NAME

ADDRESS

EMAIL

PHONE (H)

PHONE (W)

FAX

CELL/PAGER

NAME

ADDRESS

EMAIL

PHONE (H)

PHONE (W)

FAX

CELL/PAGER

NAME

ADDRESS

EMAIL

PHONE (H)

PHONE (W)

FAX

CELL/PAGER

NAME

ADDRESS

EMAIL

PHONE (H)

PHONE (W)

FAX

CELL/PAGER

NAME

ADDRESS

EMAIL

PHONE (H)

PHONE (W)

FAX

CELL/PAGER

NAME

ADDRESS

EMAIL

PHONE (H)

PHONE (W)

FAX

CELL/PAGER

NAME

ADDRESS

EMAIL

PHONE (H)

PHONE (W)

FAX

CELL/PAGER

NAME

ADDRESS

EMAIL

PHONE (H)

PHONE (W)

FAX

CELL/PAGER

NAME

ADDRESS

EMAIL

PHONE (H)

PHONE (W)

FAX

CELL/PAGER

NAME

ADDRESS

EMAIL

PHONE (H)

PHONE (W)

FAX

CELL/PAGER

NAME

ADDRESS

EMAIL

PHONE (H)

PHONE (W)

FAX

CELL/PAGER

NAME

ADDRESS

EMAIL

PHONE (H)

PHONE (W)

FAX

CELL/PAGER

NAME

ADDRESS

EMAIL

PHONE (H)

PHONE (W)

FAX

CELL/PAGER

NAME

ADDRESS

EMAIL

PHONE (H)

PHONE (W)

FAX

CELL/PAGER

NAME   PHONE (H)

ADDRESS   PHONE (W)

                                              FAX

EMAIL   CELL/PAGER

NAME   PHONE (H)

ADDRESS   PHONE (W)

                                              FAX

EMAIL   CELL/PAGER

NAME   PHONE (H)

ADDRESS   PHONE (W)

                                              FAX

EMAIL   CELL/PAGER

NAME   PHONE (H)

ADDRESS   PHONE (W)

                                              FAX

EMAIL   CELL/PAGER

NAME   PHONE (H)

ADDRESS   PHONE (W)

                                              FAX

EMAIL   CELL/PAGER

NAME   PHONE (H)

ADDRESS   PHONE (W)

                                              FAX

EMAIL   CELL/PAGER

· · · · IN FAIRYLAND, 1897 · · · ·

PENCIL AND WATERCOLOR, 37 x 17.6 CM (14½ x 6⅞ IN.)
PRIVATE COLLECTION

NAME

ADDRESS

EMAIL

PHONE (H)

PHONE (W)

FAX

CELL/PAGER

NAME

ADDRESS

EMAIL

PHONE (H)

PHONE (W)

FAX

CELL/PAGER

NAME

ADDRESS

EMAIL

PHONE (H)

PHONE (W)

FAX

CELL/PAGER

NAME

ADDRESS

EMAIL

PHONE (H)

PHONE (W)

FAX

CELL/PAGER

NAME

ADDRESS

EMAIL

PHONE (H)

PHONE (W)

FAX

CELL/PAGER

NAME

ADDRESS

EMAIL

PHONE (H)

PHONE (W)

FAX

CELL/PAGER

NAME	PHONE (H)
ADDRESS	PHONE (W)
	FAX
EMAIL	CELL/PAGER

NAME	PHONE (H)
ADDRESS	PHONE (W)
	FAX
EMAIL	CELL/PAGER

NAME	PHONE (H)
ADDRESS	PHONE (W)
	FAX
EMAIL	CELL/PAGER

NAME	PHONE (H)
ADDRESS	PHONE (W)
	FAX
EMAIL	CELL/PAGER

NAME	PHONE (H)
ADDRESS	PHONE (W)
	FAX
EMAIL	CELL/PAGER

NAME	PHONE (H)
ADDRESS	PHONE (W)
	FAX
EMAIL	CELL/PAGER

NAME _____ PHONE (H) _____

ADDRESS _____ PHONE (W) _____

_____ FAX _____

EMAIL _____ CELL/PAGER _____

NAME _____ PHONE (H) _____

ADDRESS _____ PHONE (W) _____

_____ FAX _____

EMAIL _____ CELL/PAGER _____

NAME _____ PHONE (H) _____

ADDRESS _____ PHONE (W) _____

_____ FAX _____

EMAIL _____ CELL/PAGER _____

NAME _____ PHONE (H) _____

ADDRESS _____ PHONE (W) _____

_____ FAX _____

EMAIL _____ CELL/PAGER _____

NAME _____ PHONE (H) _____

ADDRESS _____ PHONE (W) _____

_____ FAX _____

EMAIL _____ CELL/PAGER _____

NAME _____ PHONE (H) _____

ADDRESS _____ PHONE (W) _____

_____ FAX _____

EMAIL _____ CELL/PAGER _____

NAME _____ PHONE (H) _____

ADDRESS _____ PHONE (W) _____

_____ FAX _____

EMAIL _____ CELL/PAGER _____

NAME _____ PHONE (H) _____

ADDRESS _____ PHONE (W) _____

_____ FAX _____

EMAIL _____ CELL/PAGER _____

NAME _____ PHONE (H) _____

ADDRESS _____ PHONE (W) _____

_____ FAX _____

EMAIL _____ CELL/PAGER _____

NAME _____ PHONE (H) _____

ADDRESS _____ PHONE (W) _____

_____ FAX _____

EMAIL _____ CELL/PAGER _____

NAME _____ PHONE (H) _____

ADDRESS _____ PHONE (W) _____

_____ FAX _____

EMAIL _____ CELL/PAGER _____

NAME _____ PHONE (H) _____

ADDRESS _____ PHONE (W) _____

_____ FAX _____

EMAIL _____ CELL/PAGER _____

• • • • WALBER/WICK, 1914 • • • •

WATERCOLOR, 28 x 38.2 CM (11 x 15 IN.)
PRIVATE COLLECTION

· · · · ᴀɴᴇᴍoɴᴇ𝘴, ᴄ. 1916 · · · ·

WATERCOLOR, 50.5 x 49.5 cm (19⅞ x 19½ in.)

PRIVATE COLLECTION

NAME	PHONE (H)
ADDRESS	PHONE (W)
	FAX
EMAIL	CELL/PAGER

NAME	PHONE (H)
ADDRESS	PHONE (W)
	FAX
EMAIL	CELL/PAGER

NAME	PHONE (H)
ADDRESS	PHONE (W)
	FAX
EMAIL	CELL/PAGER

NAME	PHONE (H)
ADDRESS	PHONE (W)
	FAX
EMAIL	CELL/PAGER

NAME	PHONE (H)
ADDRESS	PHONE (W)
	FAX
EMAIL	CELL/PAGER

NAME	PHONE (H)
ADDRESS	PHONE (W)
	FAX
EMAIL	CELL/PAGER

NAME

ADDRESS

EMAIL

PHONE (H)

PHONE (W)

FAX

CELL/PAGER

NAME

ADDRESS

EMAIL

PHONE (H)

PHONE (W)

FAX

CELL/PAGER

NAME

ADDRESS

EMAIL

PHONE (H)

PHONE (W)

FAX

CELL/PAGER

NAME

ADDRESS

EMAIL

PHONE (H)

PHONE (W)

FAX

CELL/PAGER

NAME

ADDRESS

EMAIL

PHONE (H)

PHONE (W)

FAX

CELL/PAGER

NAME

ADDRESS

EMAIL

PHONE (H)

PHONE (W)

FAX

CELL/PAGER

NAME   PHONE (H)

ADDRESS   PHONE (W)

FAX

EMAIL   CELL/PAGER

NAME   PHONE (H)

ADDRESS   PHONE (W)

FAX

EMAIL   CELL/PAGER

NAME   PHONE (H)

ADDRESS   PHONE (W)

FAX

EMAIL   CELL/PAGER

NAME   PHONE (H)

ADDRESS   PHONE (W)

FAX

EMAIL   CELL/PAGER

NAME   PHONE (H)

ADDRESS   PHONE (W)

FAX

EMAIL   CELL/PAGER

NAME   PHONE (H)

ADDRESS   PHONE (W)

FAX

EMAIL   CELL/PAGER

NAME   PHONE (H)

ADDRESS   PHONE (W)

                                              FAX

EMAIL   CELL/PAGER

NAME   PHONE (H)

ADDRESS   PHONE (W)

                                              FAX

EMAIL   CELL/PAGER

NAME   PHONE (H)

ADDRESS   PHONE (W)

                                              FAX

EMAIL   CELL/PAGER

NAME   PHONE (H)

ADDRESS   PHONE (W)

                                              FAX

EMAIL   CELL/PAGER

NAME   PHONE (H)

ADDRESS   PHONE (W)

                                              FAX

EMAIL   CELL/PAGER

NAME   PHONE (H)

ADDRESS   PHONE (W)

                                              FAX

EMAIL   CELL/PAGER

• • • • BOULTENÈRE, c. 1924–1927 • • • •

WATERCOLOR, 44.7 x 44.7 cm (17½ x 17½ in.)

PRIVATE COLLECTION

• • • • ANEMONE AND PASQUE, WALBERSWICK, 1915 • • • •

PENCIL AND WATERCOLOR, 26.3 x 20.8 CM (10⅜ x 8³⁄₁₆ IN.)

COLLECTION: BRITISH MUSEUM

NAME   PHONE (H)

ADDRESS   PHONE (W)

                                    FAX

EMAIL   CELL/PAGER

NAME   PHONE (H)

ADDRESS   PHONE (W)

                                    FAX

EMAIL   CELL/PAGER

NAME   PHONE (H)

ADDRESS   PHONE (W)

                                    FAX

EMAIL   CELL/PAGER

NAME   PHONE (H)

ADDRESS   PHONE (W)

                                    FAX

EMAIL   CELL/PAGER

NAME   PHONE (H)

ADDRESS   PHONE (W)

                                    FAX

EMAIL   CELL/PAGER

NAME   PHONE (H)

ADDRESS   PHONE (W)

                                    FAX

EMAIL   CELL/PAGER

NAME

ADDRESS

EMAIL

PHONE (H)

PHONE (W)

FAX

CELL/PAGER

NAME

ADDRESS

EMAIL

PHONE (H)

PHONE (W)

FAX

CELL/PAGER

NAME

ADDRESS

EMAIL

PHONE (H)

PHONE (W)

FAX

CELL/PAGER

NAME

ADDRESS

EMAIL

PHONE (H)

PHONE (W)

FAX

CELL/PAGER

NAME

ADDRESS

EMAIL

PHONE (H)

PHONE (W)

FAX

CELL/PAGER

NAME

ADDRESS

EMAIL

PHONE (H)

PHONE (W)

FAX

CELL/PAGER

THE ROCKS, 1927

WATERCOLOR, 30.5 x 36.8 cm (12 x 14½ in.)
PRIVATE COLLECTION

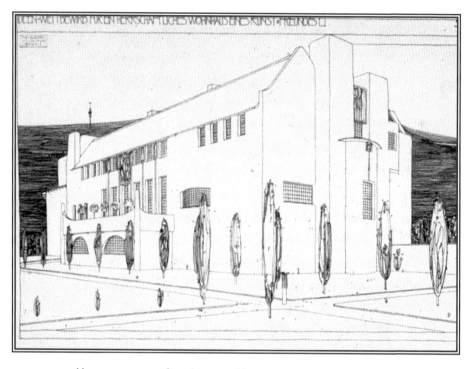

· · · · HOUSE FOR AN ART LOVER: VIEW FROM THE SOUTHEAST · · · ·
LITHOGRAPH OF MACKINTOSH'S ORIGINAL COMPETITION DRAWING, PART OF THE PORTFOLIO PUBLISHED
BY ALEXANDER KOCH IN 1902

NAME

ADDRESS

EMAIL

PHONE (H)

PHONE (W)

FAX

CELL/PAGER

NAME

ADDRESS

EMAIL

PHONE (H)

PHONE (W)

FAX

CELL/PAGER

NAME

ADDRESS

EMAIL

PHONE (H)

PHONE (W)

FAX

CELL/PAGER

NAME

ADDRESS

EMAIL

PHONE (H)

PHONE (W)

FAX

CELL/PAGER

NAME

ADDRESS

EMAIL

PHONE (H)

PHONE (W)

FAX

CELL/PAGER

NAME

ADDRESS

EMAIL

PHONE (H)

PHONE (W)

FAX

CELL/PAGER

NAME   PHONE (H)

ADDRESS   PHONE (W)

                                              FAX

EMAIL   CELL/PAGER

NAME   PHONE (H)

ADDRESS   PHONE (W)

                                              FAX

EMAIL   CELL/PAGER

NAME   PHONE (H)

ADDRESS   PHONE (W)

                                              FAX

EMAIL   CELL/PAGER

NAME   PHONE (H)

ADDRESS   PHONE (W)

                                              FAX

EMAIL   CELL/PAGER

NAME   PHONE (H)

ADDRESS   PHONE (W)

                                              FAX

EMAIL   CELL/PAGER

NAME   PHONE (H)

ADDRESS   PHONE (W)

                                              FAX

EMAIL   CELL/PAGER

NAME

ADDRESS

EMAIL

PHONE (H)

PHONE (W)

FAX

CELL/PAGER

NAME

ADDRESS

EMAIL

PHONE (H)

PHONE (W)

FAX

CELL/PAGER

NAME

ADDRESS

EMAIL

PHONE (H)

PHONE (W)

FAX

CELL/PAGER

NAME

ADDRESS

EMAIL

PHONE (H)

PHONE (W)

FAX

CELL/PAGER

NAME

ADDRESS

EMAIL

PHONE (H)

PHONE (W)

FAX

CELL/PAGER

NAME

ADDRESS

EMAIL

PHONE (H)

PHONE (W)

FAX

CELL/PAGER

NAME

ADDRESS

EMAIL

PHONE (H)

PHONE (W)

FAX

CELL/PAGER

NAME

ADDRESS

EMAIL

PHONE (H)

PHONE (W)

FAX

CELL/PAGER

NAME

ADDRESS

EMAIL

PHONE (H)

PHONE (W)

FAX

CELL/PAGER

NAME

ADDRESS

EMAIL

PHONE (H)

PHONE (W)

FAX

CELL/PAGER

NAME

ADDRESS

EMAIL

PHONE (H)

PHONE (W)

FAX

CELL/PAGER

NAME

ADDRESS

EMAIL

PHONE (H)

PHONE (W)

FAX

CELL/PAGER

• • • • PORT VENDRES, C. 1926–1927 • • • •

WATERCOLOR, 27.6 x 37.8 cm (10⅞ x 14⅞ in.)
COLLECTION: BRITISH MUSEUM

• • • • PORT VENDRES, c. 1924–1926 • • • •

WATERCOLOR, 28.8 x 39.6 CM (11⅜ x 15⅝ IN.)
PRIVATE COLLECTION

NAME

ADDRESS

EMAIL

PHONE (H)

PHONE (W)

FAX

CELL/PAGER

NAME

ADDRESS

EMAIL

PHONE (H)

PHONE (W)

FAX

CELL/PAGER

NAME

ADDRESS

EMAIL

PHONE (H)

PHONE (W)

FAX

CELL/PAGER

NAME

ADDRESS

EMAIL

PHONE (H)

PHONE (W)

FAX

CELL/PAGER

NAME

ADDRESS

EMAIL

PHONE (H)

PHONE (W)

FAX

CELL/PAGER

NAME

ADDRESS

EMAIL

PHONE (H)

PHONE (W)

FAX

CELL/PAGER

NAME

ADDRESS

EMAIL

PHONE (H)

PHONE (W)

FAX

CELL/PAGER

NAME

ADDRESS

EMAIL

PHONE (H)

PHONE (W)

FAX

CELL/PAGER

NAME

ADDRESS

EMAIL

PHONE (H)

PHONE (W)

FAX

CELL/PAGER

NAME

ADDRESS

EMAIL

PHONE (H)

PHONE (W)

FAX

CELL/PAGER

NAME   PHONE (H)

ADDRESS   PHONE (W)

                                                  FAX

EMAIL   CELL/PAGER

NAME   PHONE (H)

ADDRESS   PHONE (W)

                                                  FAX

EMAIL   CELL/PAGER

NAME   PHONE (H)

ADDRESS   PHONE (W)

                                                  FAX

EMAIL   CELL/PAGER

NAME   PHONE (H)

ADDRESS   PHONE (W)

                                                  FAX

EMAIL   CELL/PAGER

NAME   PHONE (H)

ADDRESS   PHONE (W)

                                                  FAX

EMAIL   CELL/PAGER

NAME   PHONE (H)

ADDRESS   PHONE (W)

                                                  FAX

EMAIL   CELL/PAGER

NAME	PHONE (H)
ADDRESS	PHONE (W)
	FAX
EMAIL	CELL/PAGER

NAME	PHONE (H)
ADDRESS	PHONE (W)
	FAX
EMAIL	CELL/PAGER

NAME	PHONE (H)
ADDRESS	PHONE (W)
	FAX
EMAIL	CELL/PAGER

NAME	PHONE (H)
ADDRESS	PHONE (W)
	FAX
EMAIL	CELL/PAGER

NAME	PHONE (H)
ADDRESS	PHONE (W)
	FAX
EMAIL	CELL/PAGER

NAME	PHONE (H)
ADDRESS	PHONE (W)
	FAX
EMAIL	CELL/PAGER

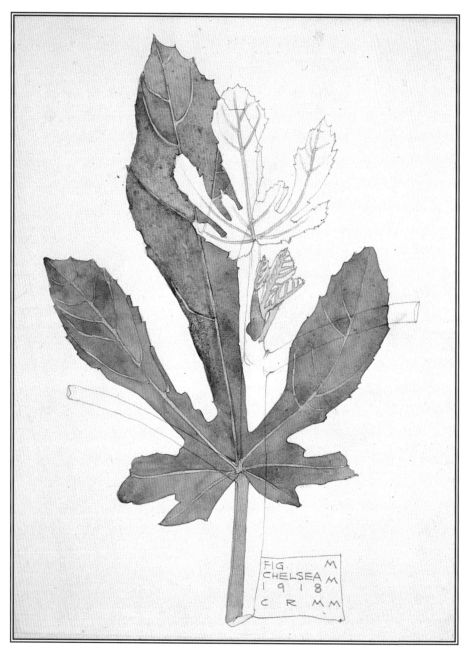

• • • • FIG LEAF, CHELSEA, 1918 • • • •

PENCIL AND WATERCOLOR, 26.2 x 20.4 cm (10⁵/₁₆ x 8 in.)
PRIVATE COLLECTION

NAME

ADDRESS

EMAIL

PHONE (H)

PHONE (W)

FAX

CELL/PAGER

NAME

ADDRESS

EMAIL

PHONE (H)

PHONE (W)

FAX

CELL/PAGER

NAME

ADDRESS

EMAIL

PHONE (H)

PHONE (W)

FAX

CELL/PAGER

NAME

ADDRESS

EMAIL

PHONE (H)

PHONE (W)

FAX

CELL/PAGER

NAME

ADDRESS

EMAIL

PHONE (H)

PHONE (W)

FAX

CELL/PAGER

NAME

ADDRESS

EMAIL

PHONE (H)

PHONE (W)

FAX

CELL/PAGER

NAME

ADDRESS

EMAIL

PHONE (H)

PHONE (W)

FAX

CELL/PAGER

NAME

ADDRESS

EMAIL

PHONE (H)

PHONE (W)

FAX

CELL/PAGER

NAME

ADDRESS

EMAIL

PHONE (H)

PHONE (W)

FAX

CELL/PAGER

NAME

ADDRESS

EMAIL

PHONE (H)

PHONE (W)

FAX

CELL/PAGER

NAME

ADDRESS

EMAIL

PHONE (H)

PHONE (W)

FAX

CELL/PAGER

NAME

ADDRESS

EMAIL

PHONE (H)

PHONE (W)

FAX

CELL/PAGER

NAME   PHONE (H)

ADDRESS   PHONE (W)

                                                  FAX

EMAIL   CELL/PAGER

NAME   PHONE (H)

ADDRESS   PHONE (W)

                                                  FAX

EMAIL   CELL/PAGER

NAME   PHONE (H)

ADDRESS   PHONE (W)

                                                  FAX

EMAIL   CELL/PAGER

NAME   PHONE (H)

ADDRESS   PHONE (W)

                                                  FAX

EMAIL   CELL/PAGER

NAME   PHONE (H)

ADDRESS   PHONE (W)

                                                  FAX

EMAIL   CELL/PAGER

NAME   PHONE (H)

ADDRESS   PHONE (W)

                                                  FAX

EMAIL   CELL/PAGER

NAME

ADDRESS

EMAIL

PHONE (H)

PHONE (W)

FAX

CELL/PAGER

NAME

ADDRESS

EMAIL

PHONE (H)

PHONE (W)

FAX

CELL/PAGER

NAME

ADDRESS

EMAIL

PHONE (H)

PHONE (W)

FAX

CELL/PAGER

NAME

ADDRESS

EMAIL

PHONE (H)

PHONE (W)

FAX

CELL/PAGER

NAME

ADDRESS

EMAIL

PHONE (H)

PHONE (W)

FAX

CELL/PAGER

NAME

ADDRESS

EMAIL

PHONE (H)

PHONE (W)

FAX

CELL/PAGER

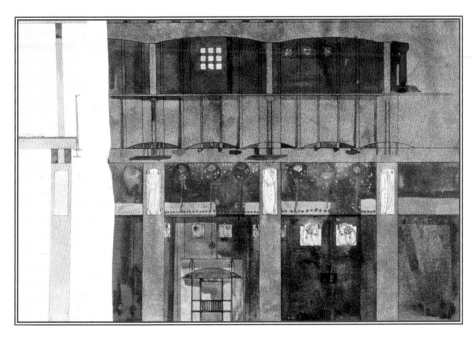

· · · · Begonias, 1916 · · · ·

PENCIL AND WATERCOLOR, 42.5 x 37.3 cm (16¾ x 14¹¹/₁₆ in.)
PRIVATE COLLECTION

NAME

ADDRESS

EMAIL

PHONE (H)

PHONE (W)

FAX

CELL/PAGER

NAME

ADDRESS

EMAIL

PHONE (H)

PHONE (W)

FAX

CELL/PAGER

NAME

ADDRESS

EMAIL

PHONE (H)

PHONE (W)

FAX

CELL/PAGER

NAME

ADDRESS

EMAIL

PHONE (H)

PHONE (W)

FAX

CELL/PAGER

NAME

ADDRESS

EMAIL

PHONE (H)

PHONE (W)

FAX

CELL/PAGER

NAME

ADDRESS

EMAIL

PHONE (H)

PHONE (W)

FAX

CELL/PAGER

NAME

ADDRESS

EMAIL

PHONE (H)

PHONE (W)

FAX

CELL/PAGER

NAME

ADDRESS

EMAIL

PHONE (H)

PHONE (W)

FAX

CELL/PAGER

NAME

ADDRESS

EMAIL

PHONE (H)

PHONE (W)

FAX

CELL/PAGER

NAME

ADDRESS

EMAIL

PHONE (H)

PHONE (W)

FAX

CELL/PAGER

NAME

ADDRESS

EMAIL

PHONE (H)

PHONE (W)

FAX

CELL/PAGER

NAME

ADDRESS

EMAIL

PHONE (H)

PHONE (W)

FAX

CELL/PAGER

NAME	PHONE (H)
ADDRESS	PHONE (W)
	FAX
EMAIL	CELL/PAGER

NAME	PHONE (H)
ADDRESS	PHONE (W)
	FAX
EMAIL	CELL/PAGER

NAME	PHONE (H)
ADDRESS	PHONE (W)
	FAX
EMAIL	CELL/PAGER

NAME	PHONE (H)
ADDRESS	PHONE (W)
	FAX
EMAIL	CELL/PAGER

NAME	PHONE (H)
ADDRESS	PHONE (W)
	FAX
EMAIL	CELL/PAGER

NAME	PHONE (H)
ADDRESS	PHONE (W)
	FAX
EMAIL	CELL/PAGER

NAME

ADDRESS

EMAIL

PHONE (H)

PHONE (W)

FAX

CELL/PAGER

NAME

ADDRESS

EMAIL

PHONE (H)

PHONE (W)

FAX

CELL/PAGER

NAME

ADDRESS

EMAIL

PHONE (H)

PHONE (W)

FAX

CELL/PAGER

NAME

ADDRESS

EMAIL

PHONE (H)

PHONE (W)

FAX

CELL/PAGER

NAME

ADDRESS

EMAIL

PHONE (H)

PHONE (W)

FAX

CELL/PAGER

NAME

ADDRESS

EMAIL

PHONE (H)

PHONE (W)

FAX

CELL/PAGER

▪ ▪ ▪ ▪ ▪ Fairies, 1898 ▪ ▪ ▪ ▪ ▪

PENCIL AND WATERCOLOR, 52.7 x 25.6 cm (20¾ x 10⅟₁₆ in.)
COLLECTION: GLASGOW SCHOOL OF ART

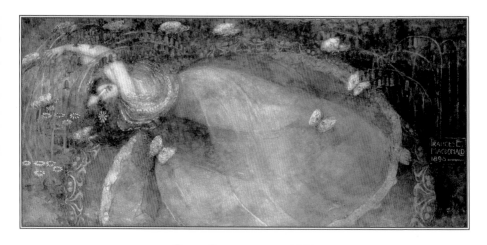

• • • • BLUE BUTTERFLIES, 1898 • • • •
FRANCES MACDONALD
WATERCOLOR, 45.3 x 101.8 CM (17¹³⁄₁₆ X 40¹⁄₁₆ IN.)
PRIVATE COLLECTION